- HERGÉ -
★

1

THE ADVENTURES OF TINTIN

KING OTTOKAR'S SCEPTRE

eih benneǩ eih bláveǩ

EGMONT

Original Album: *King Ottokar's Sceptre*
Renewed Art Copyright © 1946, 1974 by Casterman, Belgium
Text Copyright © 1975 by Egmont UK Limited

Translated by Leslie Lonsdale-Cooper and Michael Turner

Additional Material
Art Copyright © Hergé/Moulinsart 2013
Text Copyright © Moulinsart 2013

www.casterman.com
www.tintin.com

UK Edition Copyright © 2013 by Egmont UK Ltd.
Published pursuant to agreement with Editions Casterman and Moulinsart S.A.

This edition published in 2013 by Egmont UK Ltd.
The Yellow Building,
1 Nicholas Road, London W11 4AN

egmont.co.uk

1 3 5 7 9 10 8 6 4 2
ISBN: 978 1 4052 6703 8

55038/1

Tintin and Snowy

Helpful Tintin doesn't think twice before returning a lost briefcase to its owner;
his faithful dog, Snowy, knows that Tintin's goodwill often leads
to new adventures!

Professor Alembick

Professor Hector Alembick is an expert in the study of wax seals.
Little does the unsuspecting professor know that he is also the key
to a ruthless plot to depose the King of Syldavia.

Thomson and Thompson

Although the dimwitted police detectives are determined to help Tintin,
it is not long before they are falling off motorcycles
and being tricked by suspicious parcels!

King Muskar XII

The just and noble King of Syldavia comes from an established lineage
of great leaders. Will King Muskar manage to overcome plotters
determined to force him from his throne?

Trovik

A key member of the criminal organisation planning to overthrow the King of Syldavia, Trovik coordinates multiple attempts to get Tintin out of the way…permanently!

Bianca Castafiore

The first time Tintin meets the opera singer from Milan,
Bianca Castafiore manages to save the reporter from an ambush.
But can Tintin survive her ear-piercing opera arias?

Colonel Boris

The trusted aide to King Muskar XII, scheming Boris uses his position
to trap Tintin. But the villain doesn't know who he is up against!

KING OTTOKAR'S SCEPTRE

It is one of the few seals we know of from that country. But there must be others, and I am going to Syldavia to study the problem on the spot.

The Syldavian Ambassador, an old friend of mine, has promised to give me letters of introduction. I hope I shall be allowed to go through the historic national archives. A cigarette? . . .

No, thank you . . . And when are you leaving?

As soon as I have found a secretary. At least, rather more than a secretary; I really need someone to take care of all the details of my journey, like hotels, passports, luggage and so on.

But I see that you have become interested in sigillography too. Let me have your name and address and I will send you my booklet: 'How to become a sigillographer.'

How very kind of you . . .

He's going . . . Quick, meet him on the stairs . . .

Steady! . . . Here he comes!

CLICK

That's a funny place to put a watch right . . .

Got it! . . . Wonderful, the way a miniature camera can be hidden in a watch . . .

Here! . . .

We'll develop the picture right away.

!?

Is it OK?

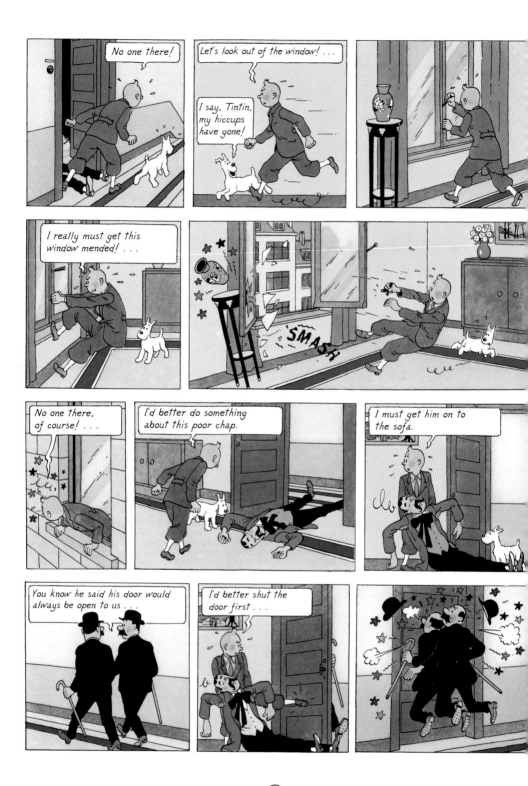

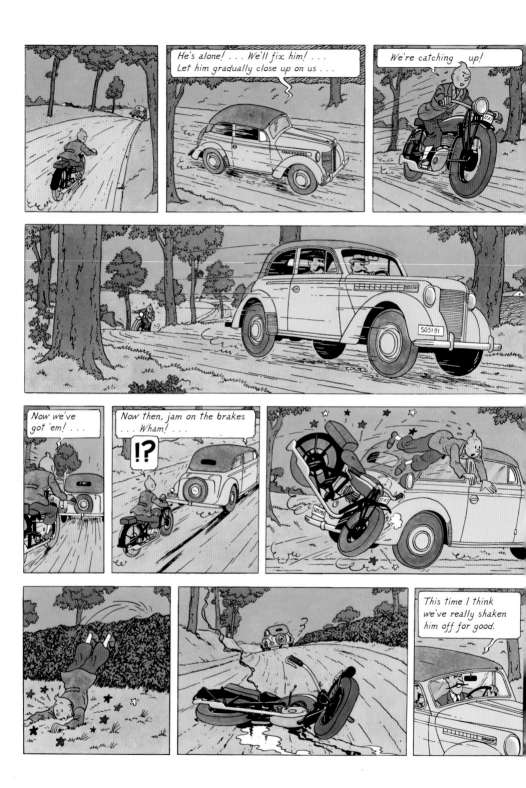

SYLDAVIA
THE KINGDOM OF THE BLACK PELICAN

AMONG the many enchanting places which deservedly attract foreign visitors with a love for picturesque ceremony and colourful folklore, there is one small country which, although relatively unknown, surpasses many others in interest. Isolated until modern times because of its inaccessible position, this country is now served by a regular air-line network, which brings it within the reach of all who love unspoiled beauty, the proverbial hospitality of a peasant people, and the charm of medieval customs which still survive despite the march of progress.

This is Syldavia.

Syldavia is a small country in Eastern Europe, comprising two great valleys: those of the river Vladir, and its tributary, the Moltus. The rivers meet at Klow, the capital (122,000 inhabitants). These valleys are flanked by wide plateaux covered with forests, and are surrounded by high, snow-capped mountains. In the fertile Syldavian plains are cornlands and cattle pastures. The subsoil is rich in minerals of all kinds.

Numerous thermal and sulphur springs gush from the earth, the chief centres being at Klow (cardiac diseases) and Kragoniedin (rheumatic complaints).

The total population is estimated to be 642,000 inhabitants.

Syldavia exports wheat, mineral-water from Klow, firewood, horses and violinists.

HISTORY OF SYLDAVIA

Until the VIth century, Syldavia was inhabited by nomadic tribes of unknown origin.

Overrun by the Slavs in the VIth century, the country was conquered in the Xth century by the Turks, who drove the Slavs into the mountains and occupied the plains.

In 1127, Hveghi, leader of a Slav tribe, swooped down from the mountains at the head of a band of partisans and fell upon isolated Turkish villages, putting all who resisted him to the sword. Thus he rapidly became master of a large part of Syldavian territory.

A great battle took place in the valley of the Moltus near Zileheroum, the Turkish capital of Syldavia, between the Turkish army and Hveghi's irregulars.

Enfeebled by long inactivity and badly led by incompetent officers, the Turkish army put up little resistance and fled in disorder.

Having vanquished the Turks, Hveghi was elected king, and given the name Muskar, that is, The Brave (Muskh: 'brave' and Kar: 'king').

The capital, Zileheroum, was renamed Klow, that is, Freetown, (Kloho: 'to free', and Ow: 'town').

Guard at the Royal Treasure House, Klow

A typical fisherman from Dhrnouk (south coast of Syldavia)

◀ *Syldavian peasant on her way to market*

A view of Niedzdrow, in the Vladir valley ▶

THE BATTLE OF ZILEHEROUM
After a XVth century miniature

H.M. King Muskar XII, the present ruler of Syldavia in the uniform of Colonel of the Guards

Muskar was a wise king who lived at peace with his neighbours, and the country prospered. He died in 1168, mourned by all his subjects.

His eldest son succeeded to the throne with the title of Muskar II. Unlike his father, Muskar II lacked authority and was unable to keep order in his kingdom. A period of anarchy replaced one of peaceful prosperity.

In the neighbouring state of Borduria the people observed Syldavia's decline, and their king profited by this opportunity to invade the country. Borduria annexed Syldavia in 1195.

For almost a century Syldavia groaned under the foreign yoke. In 1275 Baron Almaszout repeated the exploits of Hveghi by coming down from the hills and routing the Bordurians in less than six months.

He was proclaimed King in 1277, taking the name of Ottokar. He was, however, much less powerful than Muskar.

The barons who had helped him in the campaign against the Bordurians forced him to grant them a charter, based on the English Magna Carta signed by King John (Lackland). This marked the beginning of the feudal system in Syldavia.

Ottokar I of Syldavia should not be confused with the Ottakars (Premysls) who were Dukes, and later Kings, of Bohemia.

This period was noteworthy for the rise in power of the nobles, who fortified their castles and maintained bands of armed mercenaries, strong enough to oppose the King's forces.

But the true founder of the kingdom of Syldavia was Ottokar IV, who ascended the throne in 1370.

From the time of his accession he initiated widespread reforms. He raised a powerful army and subdued the arrogant nobles, confiscating their wealth.

He fostered the advancement of the arts, of letters, commerce and agriculture.

He united the whole nation and gave it that security, both at home and abroad, so necessary for the renewal of prosperity.

It was he who pronounced those famous words: '*Eih bennek, eih blavek*', which have become the motto of Syldavia.

The origin of this saying is as follows:

One day Baron Staszrvich, son of one of the dispossessed nobles whose lands had been forfeited to the crown, came before the sovereign and recklessly claimed the throne of Syldavia.

The King listened in silence, but when the presumptuous baron's speech ended with a demand that he deliver up his sceptre, the King rose and cried fiercely: 'Come and get it!'

Mad with rage, the young baron drew his sword, and before the retainers could intervene, fell upon the King.

The King stepped swiftly aside, and as his adversary passed him, carried forward by the impetus of his charge, Ottokar struck him a blow on the head with the sceptre, laying him low and at the same time crying in Syldavian: '*Eih bennek, eih blavek*!', which can be said to mean: 'If you gather thistles, expect prickles'. And turning to his astonished court he said: '*Honi soit qui mal y pense*!'

Then, gazing intently at his sceptre, he addressed it in the following words: 'O Sceptre, thou hast saved my life. Be henceforward the true symbol of Syldavian Kingship. Woe to the king who loses thee, for I declare that such a man shall be unworthy to rule thereafter.'

And from that time, every year on St.Vladimir's Day each successor of Ottokar IV has made a great ceremonial tour of his capital.

He bears in his hand the historic sceptre, without which he would lose the right to rule; as he passes, the people sing the famous anthem:

Syldavians unite!
Praise our King's might:
The Sceptre his right!

Right: The sceptre of Ottokar IV

Below: An illuminated page from 'The Memorable Deeds of Ottokar IV', a XIVth century manuscript

My aeroplane ... BRRRR ...
I fell ... Crash! ... Into the
straw ...

Czestot wzryzkar nietz on vaghabontz! ...
Czestot bätczer yhzer kzömmetz noh dascz
politzski? ...

Snowy! Snowy!

Wooah!
Wooah!

Kzommet micz omhz, noh dascz
politzski!

Come with you to
the police? ... With
pleasurski! ... I've
got a complaint to
make!

Captain, what I have to say is of
the utmost importance ... May I
speak to you in private? ...

Er ... Yes ...
Leave us alone
...

First, may I ask you a question? ...
I read in a brochure about Syldavia
that if your King loses his sceptre
he will be forced to abdicate. Is that
true? ...

As a matter of fact it is ...
But how does this concern you?

I'll tell you. I am certain there's a
conspiracy against King Muskar XII,
and that certain people will try to
steal the sceptre from him!

What's that you say? ...
What makes you imagine
such a thing?

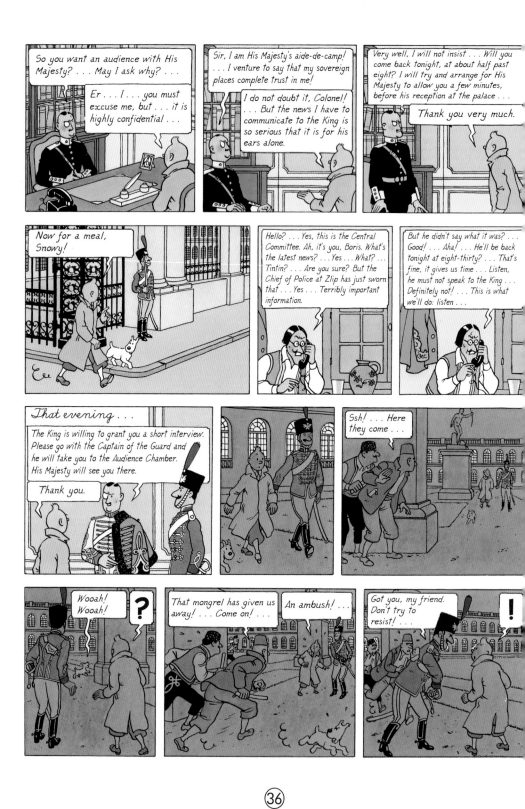

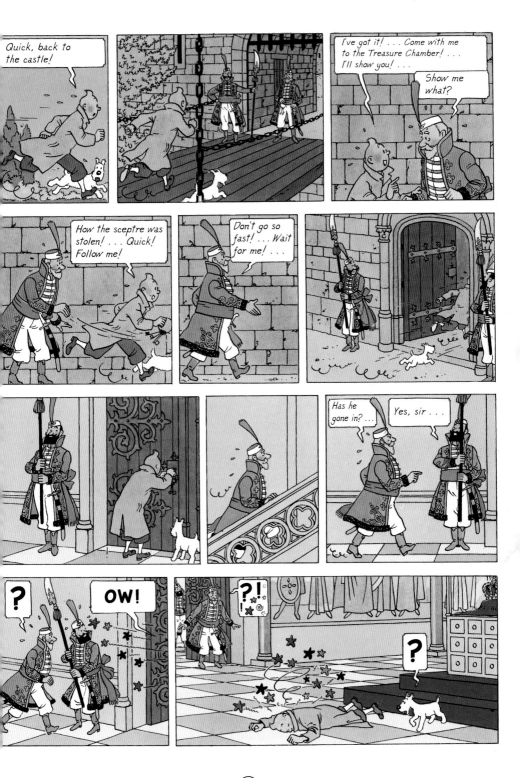

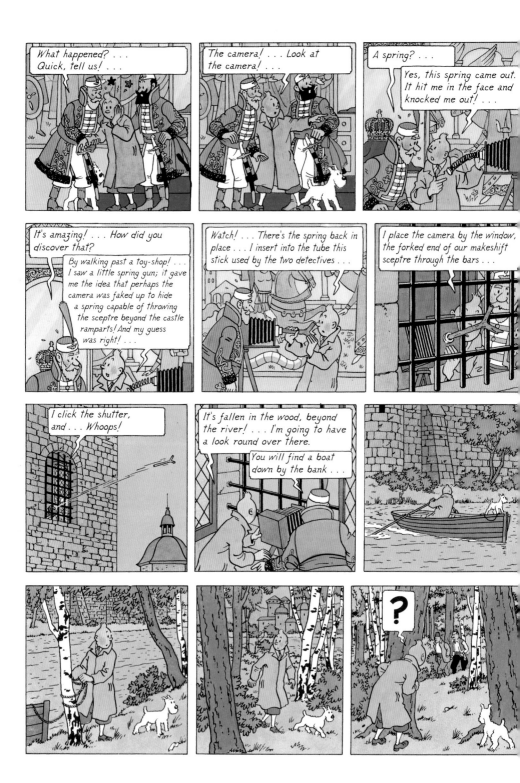

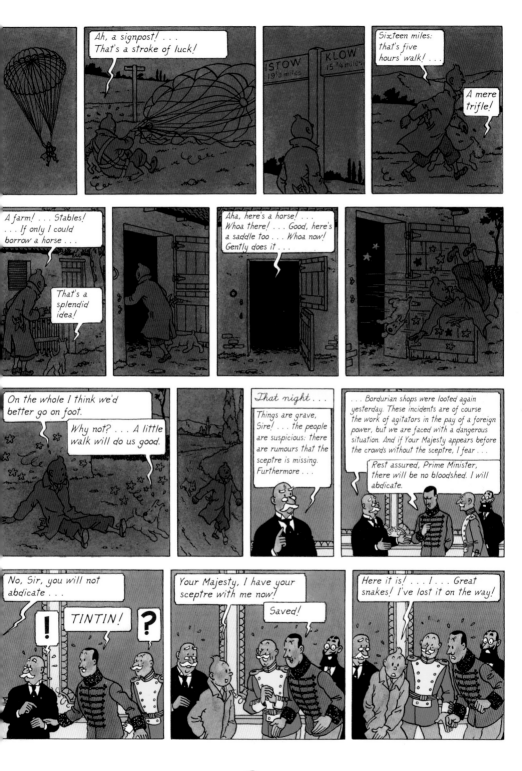

Come in!

Oh, it's you! ...What is all that firing for?

That? ...

They are firing a salute for St. Vladimir's Day ... Hurry up and dress, or we shall miss the procession.

And so the royal carriage leaves the palace ... the King, smiling, bare-headed, is holding the sceptre of Ottokar in his hand ... A great roar of welcome greets His Majesty, a roar which fades only when the strains of our national anthem swell from a thousand voices ...

And now the King is once more in his palace. Time and again the delirious crowds have called His Majesty back on to the balcony to receive their tumultuous acclaim. But now he is seated here in the Throne Room, where an investiture is taking place ...

Twins! . . . I might have guessed it! . . .
But what happened to the real professor? . . .

Well, I've just read the London newspapers. Listen: 'During a search carried out yesterday in a house occupied by Syldavian nationals, the police found Professor Alembick, the scholar. He had been imprisoned in a cellar for some weeks. He said he had been kidnapped on the eve of his departure for Syldavia, and his passport was taken . . .'

Now I see it all! First the shouts on the telephone; then the professor not wearing his glasses, and not smoking any more . . . It explains everything.

Meanwhile at Bordurian military headquarters . . .

. . . to prove our peaceful intentions, despite the inexplicable attitude of the Syldavians, I have ordered our troops to withdraw fifteen miles from the frontier . . .

Next day . . .

In a private audience this morning the King received Mr Tintin, Mr Thomson and Mr Thompson, who paid their respects before leaving Syldavia. Afterwards the party left by road for Douma, where they embarked in a flying boat of the regular Douma-Southampton service . . .

RADIO KLOW
SZOHT-SILENCE

Some hours later . . .

Ten past six.
We're there . . .

!

!

Goodness, what on earth's happening? . . .

We're falling into the sea . . .

THE REAL-LIFE INSPIRATION BEHIND TINTIN'S ADVENTURES

Written by Stuart Tett
with the collaboration of Studio Moulinsart.

Discover something new and exciting

HERGÉ

Childhood

In *King Ottokar's Sceptre* we catch a glimpse of Hergé's sensitivity toward pompous music. Perhaps the author's aversion to opera can be traced to his childhood? The photo on the left shows Georges Remi in 1912. His mother liked to let his hair grow!

In 1910, when he was three years old, Hergé's parents took him to the World's Fair, a large exhibition being held in Brussels. They were relaxing in the German section of the exhibition when a brass band started playing loud "oompah" music. It was too much for the young child; he kicked and screamed, and there was nothing that could be done. It looks like the future Hergé was forever affected by this tuneful trauma!

Perhaps Captain Haddock's destruction of an orchestra in *The Seven Crystal Balls* is no accident. Was Hergé getting his revenge, many years after the World's Fair?

bout Tintin and his creator Hergé!

TINTIN

Anyway, we know his name is Tintin.

Inspiration

Your Young Readers Editions tell you all about the inspiration behind Tintin's adventures, but what about the inspiration behind the character of Tintin himself?

Albert Londres

Hergé's first job was working in the office of the newspaper *Le Vingtième Siècle* (meaning "the twentieth century"). He read the news and followed reports written by the French journalist Albert Londres (1884–1932). Londres was one of the founders of investigative journalism, reporting news gleaned from careful, and sometimes undercover, research. His dedication to getting the true inside story led Londres on many adventures, just like Tintin!

As for Tintin's physical appearance, it is likely that Hergé was inspired by the slim build and blond hair (sometimes styled into a quiff!) of his younger brother, Paul Remi.

Hergé's brother, Paul Remi

THE TRUE STORY
...behind *King Ottokar's Sceptre*

The big question in many people's minds after reading *King Ottokar's Sceptre* is "Where exactly is the country of Syldavia?" Over the next few pages we will try to find out!

... And this is a very unusual seal, which I found quite by chance in Prague. It is the seal of Ottokar IV, King of Syldavia ...

Oh?...

The story begins when Tintin, doing his good deed for the day, returns a lost briefcase to its rightful owner. Professor Alembick invites Tintin in and shows the curious young reporter his collection of antique seals.

Once upon a time...

The use of wax seals—blobs of hot wax stamped with initials or logos—to authenticate documents arose in Europe in around the seventh century. Check out the antique seals below: do any look like the seal of Syldavia?

There are, in fact, thousands of seals, and many look similar. But perhaps there is another clue to the real-life model for Syldavia—in its coat of arms.

Thirteenth-century seal used by Sophie of Thuringia, the Duchess of Brabant.

Thirteenth-century seal used by the canon of a church in Liège, Belgium.

The seal of a real King Ottokar—Ottokar II of Bohemia (1233–1278).

Coat of arms

Hergé created a coat of arms—a type of logo used to represent a country, family, individual or organisation—for Syldavia. On this page you can find out more about the design of coats of arms and see some real-life examples of these fascinating symbols, which were first used by knights and rulers in the twelfth century.

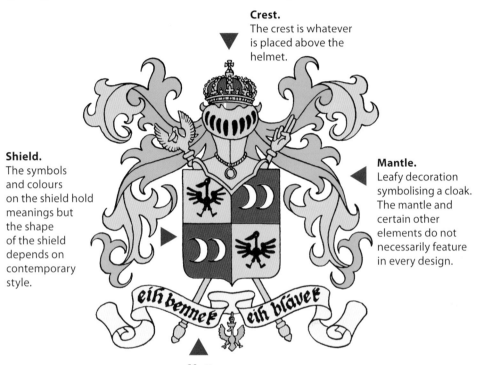

Crest.
The crest is whatever is placed above the helmet.

Shield.
The symbols and colours on the shield hold meanings but the shape of the shield depends on contemporary style.

Mantle.
Leafy decoration symbolising a cloak. The mantle and certain other elements do not necessarily feature in every design.

Motto.
A key phrase summing up the spirit of the arms-bearer.

The coat of arms of the Dutch municipality of Wassenaar.

The coat of arms of the Swiss town of Hittnau.

A Polish coat of arms dating back to the sixteenth century.

The Belgian coat of arms. The motto means "Strength in Union".

The history of Syldavia

Hergé kindly went so far as to include a full travel brochure in *King Ottokar's Sceptre* (pages 19–21) just so readers could learn about Syldavia. One of the pages of the brochure is an illustration of the twelfth-century battle of Zileheroum, in which the Slavs vanquished the Turks. Hergé based his drawing on real antique paintings called miniatures.

Fifteenth-century miniature from Mongolia.

Once upon a time...

When Hergé wrote about the Turks invading Syldavia in the tenth century, he was mirroring the real-life expansion of the Islamic Ottoman Empire between the fourteenth and sixteenth centuries. But in the end the Ottoman Empire swallowed up dozens of countries...which makes the comparison less useful when trying to pinpoint the location of Syldavia.

Fourteenth-century manuscript

There is one part of the brochure that is not in English: an extract from a manuscript entitled *The Memorable Deeds of Ottokar IV*. Hergé cleverly rearranged words from Brusseleir—the Brussels dialect he knew and had already used in *The Broken Ear* (check out the Young Readers Edition of that story)—to create a medieval Syldavian script. Perhaps this text will give us a clue to the location of Syldavia in Europe? Check out the (very rough) translation below!

"Ottokar, you are a false king, so your throne is mine."
"Really?" said King Ottokar. "Come and get it then!"
Then the king bit Baron Staszrvich on the head.
Pathetic Staszrvich bleated, "Oh!" and then the nanny goat fell to the floor.

Well, that wasn't very helpful! As for what King Ottokar IV of Syldavia is saying in the picture, "Eih bennek eih blāvek" translates as "Here I am, here I stay," although the English translators of Tintin changed the motto to "If you gather thistles, expect prickles."

Crash landing

Tintin has just had a lucky escape, landing in a pile of hay when he let go of his parachute! Some helpful locals show him the way to the police station.

Hergé kept a photo (shown below) of the Bosnian town of Mostar in his archives. Check out the red-tiled roofs and minarets. It looks like Mostar inspired Hergé's Syldavian village. Perhaps Syldavia is modelled on Bosnia?

Once upon a time...

Like Syldavia, many hundreds of years ago Bosnia was ruled by Slavic tribes. In the fifteenth century, the country was conquered by the Ottoman Empire. The Turkish conquest of Syldavia reflects this, although Hergé locates the event in the tenth century.

Further east

Yet while there are similarities between Bosnia and Syldavia, Romanian Tintin expert Dodo Niță believes that Syldavia is based on the Eastern European country of Romania.

Niță suggests that the name Syldavia is made up from the names of the two historical Romanian provinces of TranSYLvania and MolDAVIA. Romania is the only place in Europe where pelicans (the symbol of Syldavia) live in the wild. The brochure states that the Syldavian subsoil is rich in minerals; uranium deposits (which help Professor Calculus fly his atomic rocket built in Syldavia in *Destination Moon*) exist under the Carpathian Mountains in Romania.

For one more similarity, check out the portrait of King Muskar XII of Syldavia above a photo of Prince Alexandru Ioan Cuza (ruler of Romania, 1862–1866), then turn the page to **Explore and Discover!**

EXPLORE AND DISCOVER

Tintin has landed (with a bump!) in Syldavia. He has a hunch that sinister forces are plotting to steal the royal sceptre in an attempt to force the king to give up his throne. Tintin sets off for Klow, the capital of Syldavia, on a mission to warn the king, but is captured by a corrupt police official.

In the meantime, cunning imposter Alfred Alembick gains entrance to the Treasure Chamber at Kropow Castle by impersonating his brother, Professor Hector Alembick.

Just when we thought that we had considered every possible real country as the source of inspiration for Syldavia, we come across Kropow Castle, which is partly based on a real castle…in Finland!

OLAVINLINNA CASTLE

★ In 1475, Erik Axelsson Tott founded a fortress, Olavinlinna Castle, in the historical province of Savonia, in what is today Northern Europe.

★ At that time the region was part of the Swedish Kingdom; Olavinlinna Castle was located near the border with Russia in an effort to deter attacks by this country.

★ The castle became a centre for trade, and in 1639 a town, Savonlinna, was founded around the castle.

★ The fortress has three stone towers, the design of which Hergé copied for Kropow Castle. These towers were built thick to withstand cannon fire.

★ Today Olavinlinna Castle hosts the annual Savonlinna Opera Festival, started in 1912 by Aino Ackté. Over the first four years of the festival, the only non-Finnish opera performed was Charles Gounod's *Faust* with its "Jewel Song", Bianca Castafiore's favourite aria! (Learn more about Bianca Castafiore on page 14!)

Ah! There's the palace!

In the story, Tintin arrives at the royal palace in Klow, Syldavia. Hergé based the palace on the real-life royal palace in Brussels, Belgium. In 1938, when Hergé was writing this story, Nazi Germany took over Austria. Belgians were worried that Belgium was next. Perhaps then Syldavia is meant to be Belgium under threat from its neighbouring country (with Borduria in place of Germany in the story).

★ The Royal Palace of Brussels is the official palace of the Belgian King.

★ The palace dates from the eighteenth century, although the facade you can see in the photo below was built by King Leopold II at the beginning of the twentieth century.

★ Prior to this palace another palace— the Coudenberg Palace—existed in the same location.

★ Five hundred years ago the Coudenberg Palace was one of the most beautiful palaces in Europe, but it burned to the ground in 1731.

★ Archaeological excavations carried out in the area over the past few decades have uncovered extensive cellars, parts of buildings and even underground medieval streets, all of which have been open to the public since 2009.

BIANCA CASTAFIORE

Tintin makes it inside the royal palace only to interrupt a performance by the opera singer Bianca Castafiore!

This is the first time that Castafiore makes an appearance in The Adventures of Tintin. In later Tintin stories she is sometimes referred to by her stage name, "The Milanese Nightingale".

Although she may be, like all good divas, prone to vanity and swooning (Tintin's surprise entrance to the royal palace sees her promptly faint), Bianca Castafiore turns out to be a loyal and brave friend to Tintin and Captain Haddock, whose name she never pronounces correctly.

I don't know why, but whenever I hear her it reminds me of a hurricane that hit my ship - when I was sailing in the West Indies some years ago . . .

But in the end Hergé leaves no room for doubt when it comes to his musical tastes: in this frame from The Seven Crystal Balls, he lets Captain Haddock speak on his behalf!

AN OPERA LEGEND

While Hergé may well have based Bianca Castafiore on opera singers in general, he was probably influenced by several real people in particular. For instance, when he was a young boy in the 1910s, his aunt would sing to the family when they visited at teatime.

But some people think that Hergé had a real opera singer in mind for Bianca Castafiore: Aino Ackté.

Ackté.

EUREKA!

The royal sceptre has been stolen! When walking past a toy shop, Tintin suddenly realises how the thieves did it. He cries "Eureka!" in excitement, but why?

Sixteenth-century engraving showing Archimedes in his bath.

The ancient Greek mathematician Archimedes (287–212 B.C.) was asked to measure the purity of a gold crown. He realised that if he knew the volume of the crown he could calculate the purity of the gold. But the crown was not a regular shape, which made measuring the volume difficult. Then, when getting into the bathtub, Archimedes realised that water in the tub was displaced in exact proportion to the volume of his body in it. So he simply measured the water displaced by the crown with a measuring jug, which gave him the crown's volume. At this point he yelled "Eureka!" meaning "I've found it!" in ancient Greek. Ever since, the word has been associated with a sudden discovery or breakthrough.

ESCAPE FROM BORDURIA!

Tintin has retrieved the sceptre but now he is trapped in Borduria. There is only one thing for it: he commandeers a Bordurian fighter plane and takes off! Hergé drew Messerschmitt Bf-109 fighter planes for the Bordurian air force.

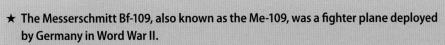

© Anto Blazevic

★ The Messerschmitt Bf-109, also known as the Me-109, was a fighter plane deployed by Germany in Word War II.

★ A total of 33,484 of these machines were built, making it the most widely-produced fighter plane ever.

★ The aircraft was advanced for its time and was designed so that important parts, such as the engine and weapons, could easily be accessed and removed for maintenance.

★ Thick bulletproof armor protected the pilot and the fuel tanks—useful features in a fighter plane!

★ More powerful versions of the aircraft with enhanced features and rearranged weaponry were created over the years: the model in this photo is a Bf-109G.

THE ROYAL PROCESSION

Tintin manages to make it back to Syldavia and returns the sceptre to its rightful owner, King Muskar XII. The royal procession takes place on St. Vladimir's Day. The magnificent carriage is based on the British Royal Family's Gold State Coach. Hergé's archives include black-and-white pictures of the coach being used for the coronation of King George V in 1911, but you can see a splendid colour photo of the coach on the right!

★ The Gold State Coach was built in 1762 in London.

★ The coach is decorated with lions' heads, cherubs, crowns, dolphins and palm trees, and is covered in gold leaf. The decoration also incorporates painted panels.

★ The coach is 23 feet long and 12 feet high, and weighs 4 tons.
It needs at least 8 horses to pull it.

★ The Gold State Coach has been used for the coronation—the crowning ceremony—of every British monarch since King George IV in 1821.

To celebrate the royal procession, there is an exciting piece of treasure waiting for you on the next page: a partially-inked sketch by Hergé showing the interior of the royal palace at Klow.
Turn the page and check it out!

The Royal Collection © Her Majesty the Queen Elizabeth II

THE THRONE ROOM

The picture on the previous pages was not used in the final version of the story, but it provides a wonderful, early and rare example of a detailed pencil sketch that Hergé left partially inked in. In the end, however, the author chose to use the perspective shown below.

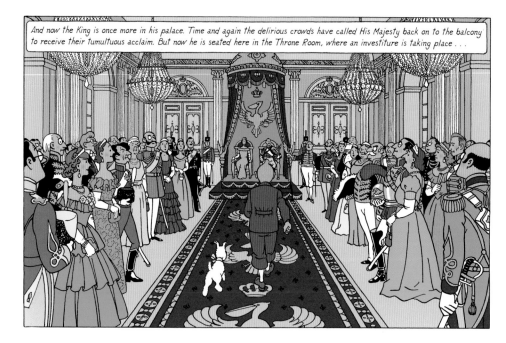

And now the King is once more in his palace. Time and again the delirious crowds have called His Majesty back on to the balcony to receive their tumultuous acclaim. But now he is seated here in the Throne Room, where an investiture is taking place . . .

FRIENDLY CROWDS

The story finishes in truly spectacular style: Tintin arrives to receive his knighthood as the royal court looks on.

Édouard Cnaepelinckx

Jacques Van Melkebeke

Marcel Stobbaerts

Edgar Pierre Jacobs

Paul Remi, Germaine Kieckens and Hergé

Hergé wanted to be present for the occasion…along with his friends! Can you spot them all in the crowd?

TINTIN'S GRAND ADVENTURE

When *King Ottokar's Sceptre* was first published, World War II was just beginning; by the end of May 1940, Belgium was occupied by Germany. Hergé was forced to make a decision. If he wanted to continue publishing Tintin stories he had to steer clear of political storylines! This was the beginning of a period during which strong themes of fantasy and exotic adventure emerged in Hergé's Tintin adventures.

Trivia: *King Ottokar's Sceptre*

Professor Alembick's collection of seals is comprehensive: experts now believe that the only known complete example of the seal of Edward the Confessor (1042–1066)—the first English monarch to use a seal—is a forgery.

For the colour version of King Ottokar's Sceptre, published in 1947, Hergé embellished Kropow Castle by adding a tower from Vyborg Castle in Russia to those based on Olavinlinna Castle in Finland.

It appears that Hergé mixed elements from many sources when he created the fictional European country of Syldavia. It is so clever that we can't say he based it on just one place!

Hergé may have been inspired by elements from the movie The Prisoner of Zenda (1937). In the film, an Englishman who resembles the king of the fictional country of Ruritania pretends to be the king at his coronation in order to save the monarchy. So in the movie the look-alike is the good guy!

The original cover for *King Ottokar's Sceptre* (1939)